STEPHEN J. ROGOWSKI

PROBLEMS for COMPUTER SOLUTION

STUDENT EDITION

Creative Computing Press   **Morristown, New Jersey**

THE AUTHOR

Stephen John Rogowski is affiliated with the State University of New York, Albany, New York. He has previously published several articles on the use of computers in education and conducted workshops in computer usage for the National Council of Teachers of Mathematics and other groups. He has also published various plotter designs in the form of posters and T-shirts.

Library of Congress Number: 79-65705
ISBN: 0-916688-13-5

Manufactured in the United States of America
Third printing July 1979
10 9 8 7 6 5 4 3

Computer enthusiasts will also want to subscribe to **Creative Computing** magazine, the #1 applications and software magazine. Subscriptions in the USA cost $15 for 12 issues; foreign $23. Sample copy $2.50 anywhere. Write to:

Creative Computing Press
P.O. Box 789-M
Morristown, NJ 07960

Preface:

This preface will serve both editions of this book. There is a student edition which contains problems to be solved, references, and an appendix of useful information.

The student edition is designed to encourage research and preliminary investigation on the part of the student. The problems are ordered by subject area, i.e., arithmetic, algebra, geometry, etc. Certain problems can be expanded, or shortened. References are given in order to encourage preliminary research.

The Teacher's Edition contains solved problems and has the following features:

(1) The student problem page is reproduced;
(2) Actual problem solutions, as printed by the computer, are given;
(3) A program which produces this solution is shown;
(4) The analysis, for most problems, is intended to make clear to the teacher exactly what went into the program, to explain any algorithm used, to give further references, and occasionally suggest further reading or research.

In some sections, more than one program has been listed. This approach is taken either to show an alternative way of solving the problem or as part of stepwise, multiple-program progression toward a solution.

The reader will find that some problems have not been either analyzed or solved. Special interest problems or problems which have never been solved, are posed to give the student an opportunity to deal with some of the unsolved problems in mathematics. Some research and an attempt to solve these will sharpen the student's insight and awareness.

The book can be used with almost any computer-oriented course of the high-school or college level. Any programming language can be used to solve the problems. However, all solutions are given here in BASIC. BASIC is the most popular and easiest to learn of the programming languages used in education.

Many problem solutions were written in EDUCOMP BASIC and run on an 8K (word) Digital Equipment Corporation PDP8 computer. Other problem solutions were implemented and run on the UNIVAC 1108 at the Computing Center of the State University of New York at Albany (SUNYA). The software was a Real-Time BASIC (RTB) package authored by personnel at the center.

Some of the programming statements used are not available on all BASIC software systems. By the same token the BASIC being used by the reader may have features which were not available to the author. An attempt has been made to point out these differences within the analysis following the program in question.

This project was made possible through a grant from the Computing Center. I wish to extend my appreciation to the staff of John Tuecke, Assistant Director for Academic Services, at SUNYA for their assistance. My thanks also to my student assistant Dave VanSchaick, who did much of the drawing and programming. Mr. Brad Longdo of the Media Center at Waterford-Halfmoon High School helped me in planning and designing many aspects of the volume.

Stephen John Rogowski

Contents

ARITHMETIC
Faulty Speedometer Spotter 1
Paper Folding Problem 2
The Sticky Salary Question 3
The First Big Deal Involving Wheat 4
You Be The Computer 5
Fibonacci And The Golden Ratio 6
Armstrong Numbers 7
The Famous Indian Problem 8
Morse Code By Computer 9
Square Roots By Iteration 10
Roman Numeral Addition and Multiplication 11
Conversion To And From Base 10 12
G. C. D. & L. C. M. 13

ALGEBRA
Two Equations And Two Unknowns 14
Sum Of The Geometric Series 15
Solution Of A Quadratic Equation 16
Algebraic Mixture Problems By Computer 17
Synthetic Division 18
Systems Of Equations Up To Four Unknowns 19
Mathematics, The Monkey And The Banana 20
Permutations And Combinations Computed 21
Generating Your Own Log Table 22
Listing Of Permutations And Combinations 23
Analysis Of A Parabola With Graph 24
Solutions To The Cubic Equation 25

GEOMETRY
The Right Triangle And The Square 26
Pythagorean Triples 27
Area Of A Polygon By A Coordinate
Geometry Method 28
Archimedian - Geometric Determination Of π ... 29
Computerized Triangular Analysis 30
Analysis Of Triangular Coordinates 31

TRIGONOMETRY
Length Of The Arc Of A Curve 32
Sine And Cosine Tables By Computer 33
Law Of Sines - Ambiguous Case 34
Resolving A System Of Vectors 35
Analysis Of Projectile Motion 36
Curve Plotting For Functions 37

NUMBER THEORY
A Quickie That May Take Awhile 38
Think Of A Number 39
Numbers: Perfect, Abundant & Deficient! 40
Arithmetic Tables Modulo N 41
Gauss - Seidel Iterative Procedure 42
Self Generating Integers 43
A Healthy List Of Prime Numbers 44
Pascal's Triangle (The Challenging Way) 45
Mersenne Primes 46
Continued Fraction Analysis 47
Extended Precision Division 48
G. H. Hardy's Dull Number! 49
Multiplication Tables In Several Bases 50
Amicable Numbers 51
Twin Prime Generator - Companion 52
The Inverse Of A Matrix 53
Magic Squares By Computer 54

Perpetual Calendar!!! 55
Arithmetic Sequences Of Primes!!! 56
Cullen Numbers 57
The Exact Digits Of N Factorial 58

PROBABILITY
Coin Flipper Simulation 59
The Old License Plate Trick!!! 60
The Telephone Book Problem 61
Generating π By Using Random Numbers On
A Circle 62
The Famous Buffon Needle Problem 63
The Matching Birthday Problem 64

STATISTICS
Correlation Study For Two Sets Of Scores 65
Statistical Analysis Of Data 66

CALCULUS
Roots Of Complex Numbers 67
Area Under A Curve Using Random Numbers 68
Area Under A Curve By The Trapezoidal Rule ... 69

SCIENCE
Einstein's Energy Equation 70
Centigrade To Farenheit And Back 71
Increase In Rest Mass As A Function Of Speed ... 72
Infinite Network Of Resistances 73

GENERAL
Love Letter!!! 74
Numeric Sorter Routine (Alphameric Option) ... 75
Touch-Tone Music By Computer 76
Music Randomly 77
Write Your Own Checks 78
Tic Tac Toe 79
Palindrome Detector 80
Metric Recipe Converter 81
The Ancient And Honorable Game Of Nim 82
Computer Poker 83
Visual Computer Timepiece 84
Melody Transposition By Computer 85
The Magic Century Mark 86
Readable Paper Output 87
Computer Verse Forms 88

UNSOLVED
One Of The Unsolved Problems Of Arithmetic! ... 89
Two More Of The Unsolved Problems
Of Arithmetic 90

APPENDIX

Pascal's Triangle, Trigonometric Generation
ASCII Character Code
Summary Of Statistical Measures
Data For Linear Regression And Correlation
Odds Against Drawing A Certain Poker Hand
ASCII Code For Eight Channel Paper Tape
Programming Tricks

BIBLIOGRAPHY

FAULTY SPEEDOMETER SPOTTER

Speedometers of cars can sometimes cost one a ticket. They
are strikingly unreliable, in some cases being off by as
much as 15 mph. The trooper, when confronted with inaccuracy
as an excuse for speeding, says "Tell it to the judge". The
judge says "Pay the fine".

An ideal way of checking your car's speedometer would be
to time the car over a measured mile (such as those between
distance markers on superhighways). If the speed is held
constant a simple table should allow one to convert the
time in seconds to a speed in miles per hour.

Program the computer to make such a table. Units are important here. Make your table from 40 seconds to 70 seconds in
divisions of one seconds. Be sure to give the speed in miles
per hour.

You may want to replace the typewriter paper with a ditto
stencil and distribute the chart to your less law-abiding
friends.

Suppose you were to fold a piece of paper a whole bunch
of times. Each successive fold should produce a piece
of paper twice as thick as the previous one.

Write a program to figure how thick the paper will be
after N folds. Assume the unfolded thickness of the
paper to be .01 inches.

Be sure to convert inches to feet when you exceed
twelve and then feet to miles when you exceed 5280 feet.
The output should include, in tabular form, the number
of folds and the thickness. Take a guess as to how
many folds it should take to produce a piece of paper
one mile thick.

The geometric series whose general term is 2^N might prove
helpful. Compare the results with the handbook values
for successive powers of two.

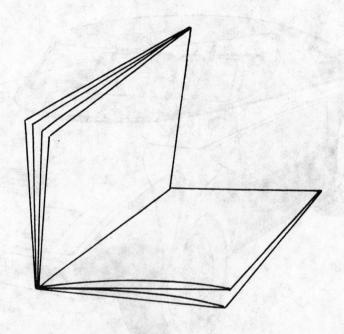

Suppose a man came to work for you. He didn't want to be paid like everyone else. He asked for a special system of payment based on doubling.

He wanted to be paid twice a month for a total of 24 pay periods per year. He wanted only 1¢ for his first pay period, 2¢ for his second pay period, 4¢ for his third, and so on, each time doubling his previous pay-check.

As an intelligent employer, you should first like to investigate the financial ramifications of this.

Program your computer to print out the man's salary for each pay period along with a running total of how much he has received to date.

The story is told of an ancient kingdom and a lazy king.
He was benevolent, well-liked and extremely fond of fun
and frolic. He had many jesters and magicians in his
court.

He came to enjoy many things. At the hand of a particular-
ly gifted mathematician he came to enjoy the intricasies of mathematics. The mathematician taught him
many tricks and games. The king quickly mastered them all.
He commissioned the man to come up with a new and challenging game and the mathematician invented CHESS.

The king was delighted, fascinated and anxious to show his
gratitude. He offered the mathematician anything in the
kingdom. The mathematician declined. The king insisted
he take something. The mathematician gave in. He said
all he wanted was a grain of wheat for as many days as
there were squares on the board. He wanted the amount
of wheat computed as follows: a single grain on the first
square, two grains on the second square, four grains on
the third square, and so on, each time doubling the amount
found on the previous square. The legend relates that at
first the king thought it a meager request for so great
a game as CHESS. He soon came to realize the enormous
and impossible order he had to fill. The legend ends
with the beheading of the mathematician .

Write a program to compute how many grains of wheat
were on each of the 64 squares of the CHESS board.
Also have the program print out a running total of the
partial sums. Compare the total amount of wheat with
the total production per year. Some say there is enough
wheat involved to cover the entire state of California
to a depth of three feet.

Suppose you find the following program lying around. Can you determine what it does to the variable N?

```
100 PRINT 'NUMBER'
110 INPUT N
120 FOR I=1 TO N
130 LET A=I*(I+1)
140 IF A=N THEN 200
150 IF A>N THEN 300
160 NEXT I
170 PRINT
200 PRINT 'ANSWER = ';I
210 GO TO 100
220 PRINT
300 PRINT 'NOT POSSIBLE'
310 GO TO 100
900 END
```

```
NUMBER
? 12
ANSWER =   3
NUMBER
? 34
NOT POSSIBLE
NUMBER
? 45
NOT POSSIBLE
NUMBER
? 23
NOT POSSIBLE
NUMBER
? 20
ANSWER =   4
NUMBER
? 68
NOT POSSIBLE
NUMBER
? 90
ANSWER =   9
NUMBER
? STOP
  PROGRAM STOPPED.
```

1   1   2   3   5   8   13   21   34   55   89 144   233   377   610   ...

Recognize the sequence of numbers listed above. It's a
Fibonacci sequence. It has a number of interesting prop-
erties.

Every term is the sum of the two preceeding it.

The product of any two adjacent terms is either one more
or one less than the two which sandwich it.

The square of any term when added to the previous term is
a Fibonacci number. (A number in the original sequence.)

How does this relate to the GOLDEN RATIO? You might first
ask what is the GOLDEN RATIO. The Greeks used the ratio
1.618 to 1 as the basis for their architecture.

Now, how are the two seemingly unrelated concepts brought
together? Well, when any term, or rather each successive
term of the sequence is multiplied by the GOLDEN RATIO
(1.618) the product gets successively closer to the next
term.

The chart below illustrates what I mean

        1 x 1.618... = 1.618 = 2 - .392
        2 x 1.618... = 3.236 = 3 + .236
        3 x 1.618... = 4.854 = 5 - .146
        5 x 1.618... = 8.090 = 8 + .090
        8 x 1.618... =12.944 =13 - .056

and we see that the deviation is decreasing.

Write a program to prove this contention true by con-
tinuing the chart until it is no longer feasible to do so.

REFERENCES:

MORE FUN WITH MATHEMATICS, J. S. Meyer, P. 51 ff, Collins
World Company, Cleveland, Ohio; 1952

TOPICS IN RECREATIONAL MATH, J. H. Caldwell, P. 12-20,
University Printing House, Cambridge, England; 1966

An n-digit number is an Armstrong number if the sum of the n-th power of the digits is equal to the original number.

For example, 371 is an Armstrong number because it has three digits such that:

$$3^3 + 7^3 + 1^3 = 371$$

Write a program to find all Armstrong numbers with 2, 3 or 4 digits.

NOTE: When the number has four digits the fourth power is used. Do a little preliminary research here in number theory to give yourself an idea of how many numbers there are.

52

8 THE FAMOUS INDIAN PROBLEM

Write a program to help the Indians out. The Indians in question are the ones who purchased Manhattan Island from the Dutch for the paltry sum of $24.00.

The sale took place in the year 1626. Suppose they had deposited the money in the local bank. Interest rates changed according to the table given below according to century.

.1600's	2%
1700's	3%
1800's	4%
1900's	5%

Figure out how much the Indians would have in the bank today. Compound the interest annually.

REFERENCE:

For Compound Formulas see CRC STANDARD MATHEMATICS TABLES, Chemical Rubber Co.; Cleveland; 1965

Write a program that will read a message from a DATA statement in <u>Morse Code</u> and translate it into English.

Have the computer type out the original coded message and
the decoded message beneath it.

Use the following alphameric code:

> . = DOT
>
> - = DASH

Find an old Boy Scout Handbook for the intricasies of the
code.

NOTE: Be sure to define and use an end of message character.
    You might also consider some uniform spacing between
    each character. Remember the computer is not capable
    of the fine lines of time interpretation that humans are.

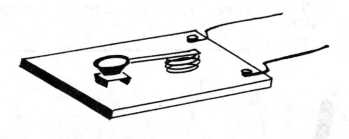

Write a program to compute the square root of any number.
Use the iterative algorithm whereby a guess is entered
along with the number to be square-rooted. Have the
computer refine that guess by division and averaging
until the square root is accurate to six decimal places.

Place a counter in the iterative loop to determine how
many iterations were required.

Compare the iterative square root to the functional square
root available in BASIC.

Extra points will be awarded for algorithms other than the
successive division one. There are some fascinating geometric
and arithmetic methods of square root computation.

REFERENCES:

Chapter on Iterative Procedures in the book PRINCIPLES OF
COMPUTATION, Peter Calingaert, p. 133, 154, Addison-Wesley
Publ. Co.; 1965

COMPUTER-ORIENTED MATH, Ladis D. Kovach, P 50-55, Holden-Day
Publ. Co.; San Francisco; 1964

Chapter 3 on "Repetitive Processes..." in COMPUTER ORIENTED
MATH by the NCTM

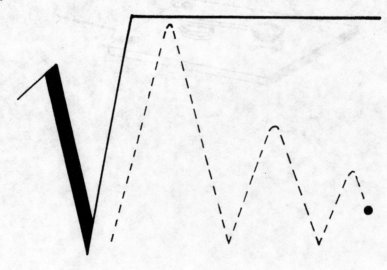

Write a program to add and multiply any two Roman numerals inputed.

Perform both operations on the numbers and print both answers in Roman form. Have the computer type out the Arabic equivalent underneath each set of operations.

In other words have the computer state the problem concisely.
For example:

$$XVII + XLIV = LXI$$

Don't feel bad here. Archimedes and others were able to do extensive calculations in this system. How thankful they would be if they could work in our modern decimal system.

NOTE: Use 2000 as your upper limit.

Write a program to take any number in base 10 and convert it to its equivalent in any base beginning with base 2. The program should also be capable of converting any number back to its base 10 (decimal) equivalent.

As input the user should include the base in current use, the desired base and perhaps the number of digits in the original number. This will simplify the computation.

Algorithms for this program are numerous. The most popular being retention of the remainders after successive divisions by the desired base. Remember, with this method, the number in question is read by listing the remainders in the reverse order of their generation.

Be careful when working in bases above base 10. Here, symbols should be used which take up only one character. Otherwise, the number 11 for example may be confused with two successive 1's.

When converting to base 10 simply generate successive powers of the base in question and multiply, then add the results to reconstruct the base 10 equivalent.

1011000 = 88

13   G. C. D. & L. C. M.

Write a program to find the G. C. D. (greatest common divisor)
and the L. C. M. (least common multiple) - sometimes called
the lowest common denominator of a set of numbers.

As input allow up to ten numbers, have the computer factor
the numbers and then use a famous algorithm - you find it -
to develop and print the G. C. D. and L. C. M.

This problem is not difficult; so try to meet the challenge
that faces every programmer - the length of the program.

Try to make the program as concise as it is efficient.

Euclid has all the hints you'll need for this one.

REFERENCES:

A PANORAMA OF NUMBERS, Robert Wisner, P. 142-152, Scott,
Foresman and Co.; Glenview, Illinois; 1970

FUNDAMENTALS OF MATHEMATICS, Edwin Stein; Allyn and Bacon;
Boston; 1967

$$2 \times 3 \times 5 \times 7 = 210$$

Write a program to solve a system of two equations in two unknowns.

Input the coefficients as given in the following scheme:

$$A*X + B*Y = C$$
$$D*X + E*Y = F$$

Have the program test for a solution first. If it is determined that a solution exists print it out. You may use one of many algorithms.

Possible solutions exist in the following areas: determinants, matrices, graphing, slopes or substitution.

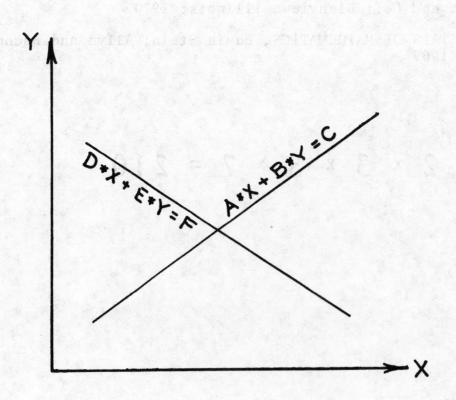

Write a program to calculate the first 50 terms of the geometric sequence given below. Use the three sets of parameters listed.

$$B + BX + BX^2 + BX^3 + \ldots + BX^{49}$$

Compare your sum with the sum given by the formula for the first N terms of a geometric series.

USE THE FOLLOWING PARAMETERS:

1)   B = 1   and   X = 1/2

2)   B = 4   and   X = 1/2

3)   B = 2   and   X = 1/4

HINT:

A loop with an accumulator is called for here.

It might look like this in BASIC:

```
65 LET M = M + Z
```

where Z is the term under computation and M is the partial sum.

Expand your program to accept any geometric or arithmetic series. The program could evaluate sums, individual terms and print out the series.

REFERENCE:

INTRODUCTION TO CALCULUS, Donald Greenspan, P. 138-42, Harper & Row, New York; 1968

Write a program to solve a quadratic equation of the form:

$$A*X^2 + B*X + C = 0$$

when A, B and C are inputed.

Be sure to test for a negative discriminant and print an appropriate warning. Also be sure to include a test for the zero denominator before the computer divides by that zero.

Use the quadratic formula to predict the exact nature of the roots before they are actually computed.

A little extra effort should enable you to have the program recognize and accommodate imaginary roots and type them out in the form

a + bi

Expand your program to include the sum and product of the roots.

Perhaps you can work backwards and print out the quadratic equation when given the sum and product of the roots.

REFERENCE:

ELEMENTARY AND INTERMEDIATE ALGEBRA TEXTBOOKS

Every algebra student has cringed at the thought of doing word problems. All word problems are not alike. Perhaps the most fearsome type are the mixture problems. Some teachers avoid them.

If you can program these type problems then you've got them licked. Write a program to solve mixture problems of the type given below.

Suppose it is desired to mix a certain amount of coffee at 69¢ per pound with 23 pounds of coffee at 98¢ per pound. We want to know how many pounds of the 69¢ coffee we will need to make a mixture which will cost 73¢ per pound.

Let any of the above quantities be available as unknowns. Do the problem in general, program it, and you'll find you've gone a long way towards understanding this type of problem.

REFERENCES: Most any elementary algebra text would have specific problems as well as examples of solution.

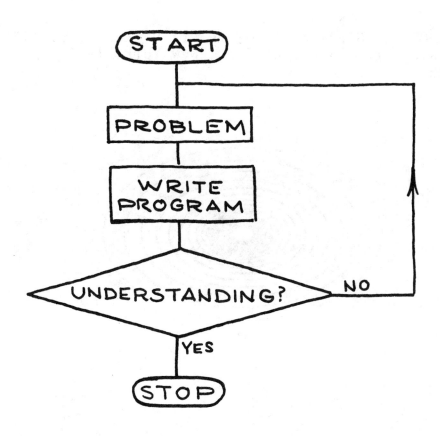

SYNTHETIC DIVISION

Synthetic division is the process of evaluating
a polynomial by guessing whether a number is a factor.
That number is then analyzed in conjunction with the
coefficients to produce a remainder and the coefficients
of the quotient. Should the remainder be zero the
original number would then be a factor. Actually
'root' is a better word here than 'factor'.

Write a computer program to perform synthetic
division on a given polynomial. Have the computer
accept the polynomial's coefficients as well as the
guess for a root. Have the computer indicate when
the remainder is zero. Have the computer type out
the quotient polynomial and the remainder if it is
non-zero. Remember the number used in the test and
the binomial factor usually differ by a sign.

Be sure to research the process carefully before
beginning.

REFERENCE: ALGEBRA & TRIGONOMETRY, M. Keedy, p. 177,
Holt, Rinehart & Winston, Inc., New York; 1967

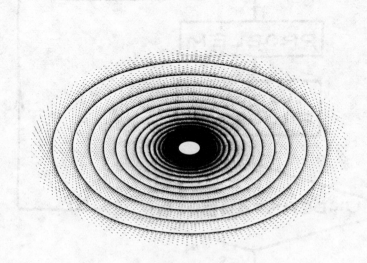

Write a program to compute how many permutations or combinations there are for N things taken R at a time.

The user should be able to specify which measure he wants. The computer should then simply print out how many. This is a simple matter of learning some formulas. These formulas contain factorials and these must be computed prior to inclusion in the final computation. The factorial computation should be done in a loop prior to the actual plugging-in to the formula.

REFERENCES:

PROBABILITY AND STATISTICS, Fred Mosteller, P. 19-47, Addison-Wesley, Reading, Mass.; 1961

INTRODUCTION TO PROBABILITY AND STATISTICS, Henry Alder, P. 60-7, W.H. Freeman & Co., San Francisco; 1962

You've all had the opportunity to make use of log tables, during your mathematical lives. Ever wonder where those tables come from. Here's a chance for you to make a set for yourself.

Limit the table to the integers between 1 and 100. Of course you may not use the built in LOG function available in BASIC. However, with the knowledge that:

$$\log_{10}x=a \qquad \text{only when } 10^a = x$$

one should easily be able to proceed by solution of that relation.

Since:

$$\log_{10} 100 = 2$$

it only stands to reason that:

$$10^2 = 100$$

Try to get the output in the following form (it's concise):

1	0	410	788	1136	1458	1758	2038	2301	2550	2785
2	3009	3221	3423	3616	3801	3978	4149	4313	4471	4623
3	4770	4913	5051	5184	5314	5440	5562	5681	5797	5910
4	6020	6127	6232	6334	6434	6532	6627	6721	6812	6902
5	6989	7075	7160	7242	7324	7403	7482	7558	7634	7708
6	7781	7853	7924	7993	8062	8129	8195	8261	8325	8388
7	8451	8512	8573	8633	8692	8751	8808	8865	8921	8976
8	9031	9085	9138	9191	9243	9294	9345	9395	9445	9494
9	9542	9590	9638	9685	9731	9777	9823	9868	9912	9956

IMPORTANT: Omit the Characteristic. You may retain the decimal point if you wish. FOUR places please.

REFERENCES:

CRC STANDARD MATHEMATICAL TABLES, Samuel Selby, P. 1-6; Chemical Rubber Co.; Cleveland, Ohio; 1965

FUN WITH MATHEMATICS, J. S. Meyer, P. 90-99; World Publ. Co.; Cleveland, Ohio; 1969

MATHEMATICS FOR STATISTICS, W. L. Bashaw, P. 253-264, John Wiley and Sons; New York 1969

There is sometimes a need to know more than just the number of combinations or permutations of a given number of elements. It is sometimes necessary to list the permutations or combinations that start with a given letter or series of letters.

Write a program to type out all possible permutations or combinations that have a certain property. Perhaps a sequence of items can be specified in a DATA statement. The program should also include the total possible permutations and combinations from the standard formula.

REFERENCES:

PROBABILITY AND STATISTICS, Fred Mostellier, P. 19-47, Addison-Wesley, Reading, Mass.; 1961

INTRODUCTION TO PROBABILITY AND STATISTICS, Henry Alder, P. 60-7, W. H. Freeman & Co., San Francisco; 1962

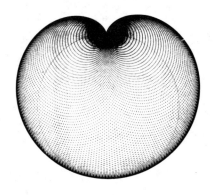

Write a program to accept the equation of any quadratic. Test the equation to see if it will produce a parabola. Reject the equation if it will not be a parabola.

Have the computer type out the zeroes of the curve; the high point or low point; the equation of the axis of symmetry; whether it is concave upward or downward; along with the sum and product of the roots. Have the computer plot the graph of the parabola indicating the zeroes of the function with symbols other than the ones you're plotting with. Have the computer include the axis of symmetry.

Be sure the roots are real before attempting solution on the real number axes. You may use the quadratic formula for the zeroes or you may wish to use a program refered to in another problem. (See ZEROES OF A FUNCTION BY ITERATION).

Do some preliminary research in an algebra text on conic sections. Save yourself some time by reducing the problem to its essentials.

REFERENCE:

ANALYTIC GEOMETRY, W. A. Wilson, P. 98-108, D. C. Heath & Co., Boston; 1949

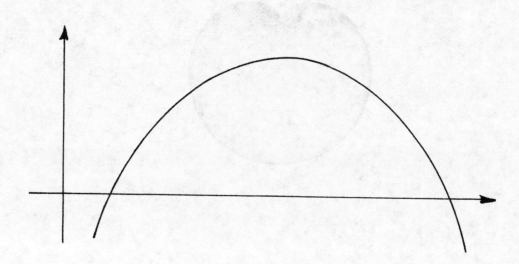

Write a program to find all the roots of a cubic equation of the form:

$$Ax^3 + Bx^2 + Cx + D = 0$$

where A, B, C and D are inputed. Remember all the roots need not be real. If only one root is real then the other two will be complex.

Reduce the cubic to a quadratic and then use the quadratic formula to find the complex roots. Be sure to express them in the form:

$$a + bi$$

Devise a test to determine the number of real roots.

REFERENCES:

Chapter 8 in BASIC PROGRAMMING by Kemeny & Kurtz, P. 50-53, Wiley & Sons, New York; 1971

Be sure to review what you've learned about cubics in an advanced secondary math text. It'll save programming time.

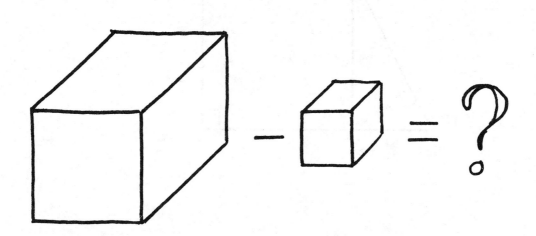

    Using the figure below find the values of 'X' and 'Y'.
Write a program to solve the problem. The program could
involve an algorithm for synthetic division (see problem
with that name) or a simple cranking out of "Pythagorean
Triples". [See problem of same name].

    A lot of preliminary work is needed here, so be sure to
reduce the problem to its programmable state. All the information necessary for the solution is given in the diagram,
believe it or not.

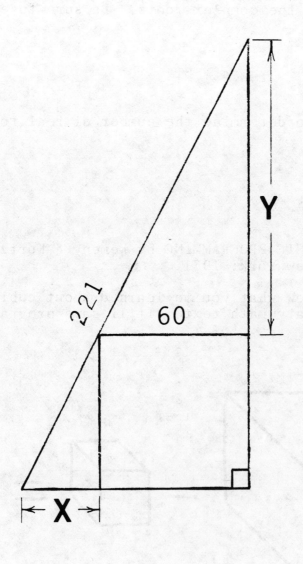

Every student knows the pythagorean theorem and its importance in working with right triangles. In fact there is hardly a student who isn't familiar with the numbers [3,4,5] or [5,12,13]. Some students know others. Few students can give more than a couple of these "Pythagorean Triples." Obviously, a "Pythagorean Triple" is a set of numbers which satisfy the relationship:

$$X^2 + Y^2 = Z^2 \quad .$$

Write a program to list as many triples of this sort as you deem feasible. A simple way would be to test all triples and PRINT only those which satisfy the theorem. This is an extremely inefficient algorithm. The computer could test as many as a million numbers before it encountered a "Pythagorean Triple."

The student is invited to find what are known as "generators", that is, algebraic expressions which when fulfilled supply the desired triples every time. One useful "generator" could be any two natural numbers 'u' and 'v' (one greater than the other), such that the sum of their squares produces one element of the triple; the difference between their squares produces a second; and twice their product produces the last. The natural numbers may differ by any number of units and it is intriguing to note the relationships which "pop up".

After you've listed the triples inspect them closely. You'll find many interesting relationships. Did you know that every set of triples has at least one element that is divisible by 3, one that is divisible by 4 and one that is divisible by 5?

REFERENCES:

INTRODUCTION TO THE THEORY OF NUMBERS, Ivan Niven, P. 1-9, John Wiley and Sons, New York; 1962

INVITATION TO NUMBER THEORY, O. Ore, Random House; 1967

THEORY OF NUMBERS, B. M. Stewart, P. 153-6, Macmillan Company, New York; 1964

Write a program to compute the area of a polygon. Assume that the polygon has a known but variable number of sides.

As input you will need the number of sides of the polygon along with the coordinates of its vertices. It will not necessarily be a regular polygon, nor will it be convex. Using only the coordinates of each vertex and the number of sides you must compute the area.

This will require an algorithm which is already in existence. The development of the algorithm for the area is not unusually difficult and can be done by you. However, you can probably find it in all but the most elementary texts on plane or coordinate geometry.

Why not test your skill at programming graphical output? Have the program plot the polygon involved.

REFERENCES:

GEOMETRY, Edwin Moise, P. 371-406, Addison-Wesley, Reading, Mass.; 1967

ANALYTICAL GEOMETRY, W. A. Wilson, P. 8-27, D.C. Heath & Co., Boston; 1949

MODERN ANALYTICAL TRIGONOMETRY, Julian Mancill, P. 27-56, Dodd, Mead & Co., New York; 1960

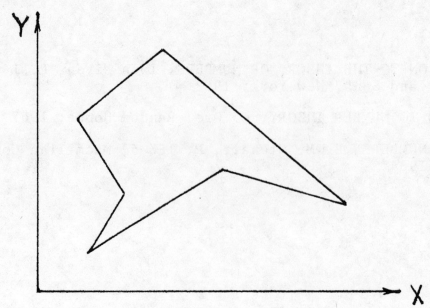

The determination of π has been a problem which fascinated mathematicians since time began.

One of the more interesting ways to generate it is that used by Archimedes. Although he did it arithmetically, as well as by other methods, this is by far his most famous.

Essentially what he did was compute the perimeters of regular polygons that were inscribed in and circumscribed about a circle. For ease of computation let your circle have a radius of one - a unit circle. The circumference will now be 2π.

Start with a square which you circumscribe about the circle. The diagonal of the inner square will equal the side of the outer square; and both will equal the diameter of the circle. The radius of the inner polygon will always be one, while the apothem of the outer polygon will always be one.

You must develop an expression for the perimeter of each polygon which involves the apothem and the radius and the number of sides.

Write a program to compute the perimeters of these polygons as their sides are successively doubled in number. It is plain that the outer perimeter will always exceed the circumference of the circle while the inscribed perimeter will always fall a bit short. The ratio of the circumference to the diameter will always contain some form of π. Compute the ratio of the perimeter to the diameter for each polygon and PRINT it. You will find that this ratio will approach π from the left and the right.

Try to avoid an algorithm which contains π. Some trigonometric expression would be desirable.

REFERENCES: MORE CHIPS FROM THE MATHEMATICAL LOG, NCTM, p. 75
"Rational Approximations of PI", A.R. Amir-Moez,
University of Oklahoma, Norman, Oklahoma; 1970

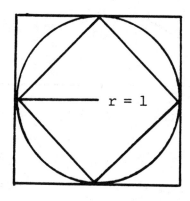

r = 1

Write a computer program to accept the coordinates of the vertices of a triangle as input.

Have the program compute the coordinates of the
intersection points of the medians, the perpendicular
bisectors of the sides, the angle bisectors and the
altitudes.

You may also want to type out the equations of
some of these lines.

When you run the program, avoid involving lines
which are vertical. These will have no slope. They
will cause an error message because of the division
by zero in your slope formula. You may wish to bypass
this technique in favor of one which does not have
this bug.

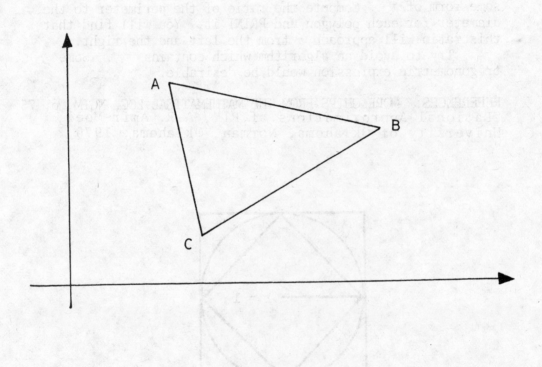

Prepare a program that will read in three sets of coordinates. Determine whether those coordinates are the vertices
of a triangle.

If they are the sides of a triangle, type out what kind:

Scalene, Isosceles, Equilateral.

Also check to see whether it is a right triangle. Have the
computer draw a picture of the triangle using the TAB (X)
function and finally compute and print the area of the triangle.

Be sure to use a general area formula and not one which only
works for specific triangles.

NOTE: You may neglect the picture plot of the triangle.

REFERENCES:

BASIC PROGRAMMING, Chapter 8, Kemeny & Kurtz, P. 47-50,
Wiley & Son, New York; 1971

MATH 10 Textbooks (Topic: Coordinate Geometry)

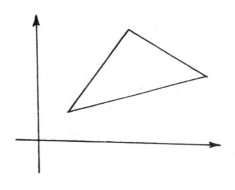

Write a program to compute the length of an arc for a given function.

Input the function in question and the limits (points) between which the length is to be computed. The input should be two numbers which will be X-values. Compute the Y-values for those points. Have the computer divide the curve into a number of sections. Each section will be curved. Approximate that curve with a secant between the endpoints of the segment. The length of the secant can be found using coordinate geometry. It will be close to the arc length. Increase the number of intervals and sum them up until the answer is accurate to a specified degree.

Try to find a formula for arc length which can be used directly. Compare your approximation with the value as computed by formula.

REFERENCE:

INTRODUCTION TO CALCULUS, Donald Greenspan, P. 206-209, Harper & Row, New York; 1968

GEOMETRY, Edwin Moise, P. 371-406, Addison-Wesley, Reading, Mass.; 1967

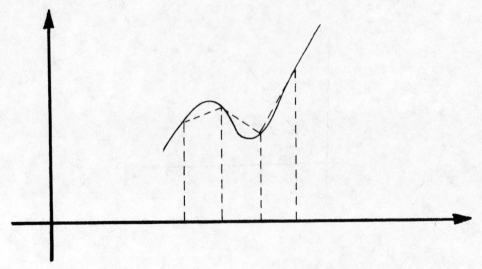

Ever wonder where Sine and Cosine tables come from? They are generated by tedious calculation using infinite series.

Use the series given below to generate a table for the sines and cosines of all angles between $0°$ and $90°$.

Careful though, the variable x in both series must be in radians or the numbers will be meaningless. You'll have to have a subroutine to convert from degrees to radians and back. NO radians allowed in the output.

You choose the final form of the table. Try to get four places of accuracy. Obviously, using the SIN and COS functions in the BASIC language is not allowed.

One more problem you'll face is that of keeping the accuracy when so many terms of the series are needed to produce four places of accuracy. To avoid roundoff error, you may have to devise a way of retaining all the significant digits of the partial sums in an array. You may use the SIN and COS built-in functions to check accuracy only.

The series to be used:

$$\sin x = x - \frac{x^3}{3!} + \frac{x^5}{5!} - \frac{x^7}{7!} + \dots$$

$$\cos x = 1 - \frac{x^2}{2!} + \frac{x^4}{4!} - \frac{x^6}{6!} + \dots$$

REFERENCES: Other series representations may be used...
They may be found in such books as:

STANDARD MATHEMATICAL TABLES, 14th Edition, CRC, P. 408 ff, Chemical Rubber Company, Cleveland, Ohio; 1965

100 GREAT PROBLEMS IN ELEMENTARY MATHEMATICS, Heinrich Dorrie, P. 59-64, Dover Publications, New York; 1965

Write a program which accepts as input two sides of a triangle and the angle opposite one of these sides.

The program should work for any type triangle oblique or right. Have the program type out the size of the third side along with how many triangles it is possible to construct with those dimensions. If the triangle is a right triangle, have the program say so.

Refer to the diagram below. Input 'A', 'B' and θ. The diagram should help you set the problem up. Use the right triangle which was constructed around the original. Involve a relationship with 'X' and 'Y' as well as 'B' and 'H'.

REFERENCE:

MODERN ANALYTICAL TRIGONOMETRY, Julian Mancill, P. 167-185, Dodd, Mead & Co., New York; 1960

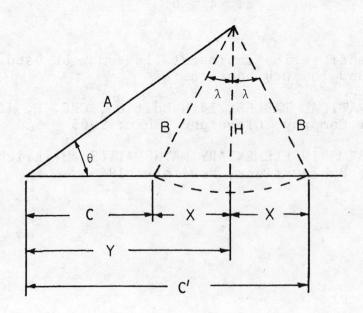

Physics students will remember the tedious calculations involved
in working out the resultant of a given set of vectors.

Assume that all vectors, up to a total of ten, originate at the
origin of a cartesian coordinate system. Using as input the magnitude and direction of each vector, write a program to compute and
plot the magnitude and direction of the resultant.
Use positive angles turned from the x-axis up to 360° as your
indication of direction.

You may wish to print out the intermediate components of each
vector in tabular form, much as we did in the solution of such problems with paper and pencil.

An actual picture of the situation from the computer would be
quite impressive also.

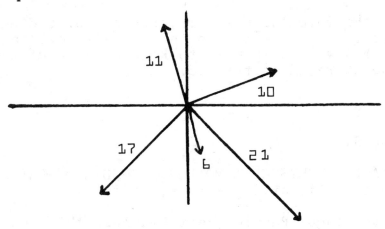

A typical system might look like this!

REFERENCES:

PHYSICS programs from the Altoona area schools.

BASIC PROGRAMMING, Kemeny and Kurtz, Chapter 16, P. 120-124,
Wiley & Sons, New York; 1971

Projectile motion is one of the more interesting branches of Physics. The tedious nature of the calculations, however, sometimes leaves students unconvinced of the foregoing assertion.

Given as input the muzzle velocity, angle of firing and other variables, program the computer to print out the range of the projectile along with the height to which it will rise, then have the computer print out a picture of the path (which we know will be a parabola).

Label both the vertical and horizontal axes with the proper units and dress the program up to be able to include two or more projectiles on one run.

Missile and missile intersection graphs are a possibility here.

Be sure the formulas used are correct for the units you introduce. You may wish to include air resistance in your study. You will then need to know more about the air such as temperature, density, etc.

REFERENCES:

UNDERSTANDING PHYSICS: MOTION, SOUND AND HEAT, Isaac Asimov, New American Library, New York; 1969

Most high school Physics texts include this topic.

Write a program to plot on the same set of axes any two pair of the functions listed below.

Look over the situation to be sure that both your vertical and horizontal plot will include any points of intersection.

As a "special", have the computer predict the points of intersection and label them with something other than the asterisks or other symbols used in the rest of the plot.

Go at least one full cycle for any function.

THE FUNCTIONS

1) sin and cosine
2) log and sin
3) $x^2 + 6x + 8$ and $y = 2x - 3$

Be sure the program is versatile enough to vary the horizontal and vertical range spacing at the programmers request.

Specify the units being used or better yet actually type them out as the axis for the plot.

You might do well to try a few of the library plot programs to see how they accomplish the task.

REFERENCES:

BASIC PROGRAMMING, Section 8.3, Kemeny & Kurtz, P. 53-55, Wiley & Son, New York; 1971

Do this one by trial and error, but give the process some thought first.

Can you find a five digit number which when multiplied by four has its digits reversed?

Essentially what we want is a number ABCDE such that:

$$4 \times ABCDE = EDCBA$$

You'll need to develop a recognition algorithm that will know when the digits of a number are the reverse of the original.

An old thought comes to mind. When a number and its "mirror image" are subtracted, one from the other the difference is always a multiple of nine. It's just a thought not necessarily a hint.

Many number games start with the phrase, "think of a number!".

Many different algorithms have been used to do this. One of them is the Chinese Remainder Theorem. Think of a number less than 316. Write down the remainders when that number is divided by 5, 7 and 9. Using only those remainders the computer should be able to reconstruct the original number.

Research the Chinese remainder theorem and write a computer program to use it to find the number someone has thought of.

REFERENCE:

ELEMENTARY THEORY OF NUMBERS, William LeVeque, P. 52, Addison-Wesley, Reading, Mass.; 1962

40 NUMBERS: PERFECT, ABUNDANT & DEFICIENT!

Write a program to test a given number to see whether it is PERFECT, ABUNDANT or DEFICIENT.

A number is:

PERFECT: when the sum of the divisors of that number
            excluding the number itself equals the number
            in question.

ABUNDANT: when the sum of the divisors exceeds the number.

DEFICIENT: when the sum of the divisors is less than the
            number.

EXAMPLES:

$6 = 1 + 2 + 3$ and is PERFECT.

$12 \neq 1 + 2 + 3 + 4 + 6$ In fact the sum exceeds 12. So
                            12 is abundant.

$10 \neq 1 + 2 + 5$ Here the sum falls short of 10. So 10
                     is deficient.

You must develop an algorithm to factor a number into its divisors. A number of them exist. Once you've completed that the rest is easy. Be sure to include 1 but exclude the number itself.

REFERENCES:

NUMBERS & MATHEMATICS by Dodge, Chapters on Number Theory, P 245-249

A PANORAMA OF NUMBERS, Robert Wisner, P.84-100; Scott, Foresman and Co.; Glenview, Illinois; 1970

RECREATIONS IN THE THEORY OF NUMBERS, A. H. Beiler, P. 11-26; Dover Publications Inc.; New York; 1964

Most any book on Number Theory would have some reliable algorithms for factorization.

Write a computer program to type out an addition table and a multiplication table modulo N, where N is any number up to 20.

Remember modulo means remainder when divided by.

For example: 17 ≡ 1 mod 4   means that when 17 is divided by 4 the remainder is 1.

Have the computer type out two separate tables, one for multiplication and one for addition. You may use the MOD function if it is available. It might be more interesting to develop your own algorithm for computing the remainder. It can be done in two lines or less.

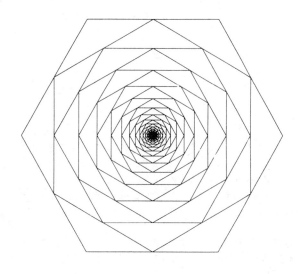

There is a technique for solving systems of equations which has probably occured to some students.

For example when solving 3 equations in 3 unknowns, why not guess at 'y' and 'z', plug these in and generate 'x'. Then take the new 'x' which is more than a guess and use the current 'z' to generate a new 'y'. Then take the generated 'x' and 'y' to generate a 'z'. This process will iterate to a solution under certain conditions.

The iteration will not converge if the coefficient matrix of the original system is not diagonally dominant. This means if the system were

$$4x + 2y - z = 11$$

$$x + 7y + 2z = 16$$

$$2x - 3y - 9z = 85$$

this system would have a solution because:

$$|4| \geq |2| + |-1| \quad \&$$

$$|7| \geq |1| + |2| \quad \&$$

$$|-9| \geq |-3| + |2|$$

In addition to these three conditions one of the above inequations must be a strict inequality. That is the left must be strictly greater than the right. Under these conditions the process will iterate to a solution.

Write a computer program to accept the equations which have been solved for the respective variables. You could even have the computer solve them. Input the coefficients and the initial guesses. Have the computer type out the approximations along the way. Include a test for convergence. Test to see whether a given value has changed in the last iteration.

Self-generating integers are whole numbers whose separate integers, when factorialized (!) each by itself and added together give the original number.

An example is not given here because there are only four such numbers known. There is one with three digits.

Write a computer program to find as many of these SGI's as you can. You must have a routine to factorialize an integer.
routine.

This is a time consuming program so be as efficient as possible. Unless you have no time limit on CPU time, you may only be able to find a few or even only one such SGI.

A HEALTHY LIST OF PRIME NUMBERS

Write a program to print in heirarchical order all prime numbers from 2 to 1000.

There is a classical algorithm for this process and you should know it.

You may not perform any multiplication or division in your program yet you will be able to generate all the primes called for in the exercise.

Print the primes horizontally, so as to conserve paper.

Remember 2 is a prime number.

HINT: Do not try to generate the primes directly. Eliminate the undesirables from your list. Let them fall through your "sieve" as it were.

REFERENCES:

A PANORAMA OF NUMBERS, Robert Wisner, Pp 67-71, Scott, Foresman and Company; Glenview, Illinois; 1970

BASIC PROGRAMMING, Kemeny and Kurtz, p. 60-63, Wiley & Sons; New York; 1971

TOPICS IN RECREATIONAL MATHEMATICS, J. H. Caldwell, p. 32-40, University Publishing Co.; Cambridge, England; 1966

Write a program to generate piece by piece the rows of Pascal's triangle.

The triangle must be isosceles and the ones along the sides must be included.

Generate at least the first seven rows. Be sure enough space is allowed for double numbers, so that the triangle will not be unduly distorted.

As you know there are many ways to generate the triangle. Combinatorial methods, trigonometric methods, the binomial theorem. Choose the one you think is best suited and proceed.

The arithmetic generation of the triangle is to be discouraged. It is long and does not require much skill.   We won't allow the first two rows to be entered so that the others can be generated by successive addition. There are too many other GOOD ways of generating it.

REFERENCES: See the sheets on Pascal's triangle in the Appendix.

A number which is prime and of the form 2^p-1 where p itself is prime is known as a Mersenne prime.

These numbers are useful in the study of perfect numbers. (See problem of that title). Each Mersenne prime of the form $2^p - 1$ produces an even perfect number of the form below and every even perfect number is of this form.

There are no known odd perfect numbers! Write a program to find several p's that yield Mersenne primes, and find the corresponding even perfect numbers.

FORM OF PERFECT NUMBER .... $2^{p-1}(2p-1)$

REFERENCES:

MORE CHIPS FROM THE MATHEMATICAL LOG, Kathy Ruckstahl and Charles Wilford, P.36-39

MATHEMATICAL RECREATIONS AND ESSAYS, Ball, MacMillan & Co., London; 1914

MATHEMATICAL RECREATIONS, Kraitchik, P. 70-73, W. W. Norton & Co. Inc., New York; 1942

A continued fraction is an ordinary fraction which has been rewritten.

For example: $\frac{7}{11}$ could be written as follows,

$$\frac{7}{11} = \frac{1}{\frac{11}{7}} = \frac{1}{1 + \frac{4}{7}} = \frac{1}{1 + \frac{1}{\frac{7}{4}}} = \ldots$$

Write a computer program to accept any rational number and convert it to continued fraction form. The output need not be in the format given above. Simple 'slashes' (/) may be used to indicate division.

It is possible to have the output as it is given above. It is most difficult, however and hardly worth the extra time.

REFERENCE:

CONTINUED FRACTIONS, A. Ya Khinchin, University of Chicago Press, Chicago; 1964

Write a program to carry out a division until it repeats. All rational numbers (fractions) can be expressed as decimals. All rational numbers repeat sooner or later.

Take a long-hard-look at the long division algorithm you are so familiar with. Program the computer to do exactly what you do when you divide.

When you get it working print out all the fractions with denominator '17'. Take a look at the pattern. Try some other prime denominators. Try to establish a pattern for these. Use the greatest integer function (INT) to devise a test for divisibility.

LEAST EXPONENTS TABLE FOR PRIME DENOMINATORS 3 TO 97

PRIME	EXPONENT	PRIME	EXPONENT
3	1	**47	46
**7	6	53	13
11	2	**59	58
13	6	**61	60
**17	16	67	33
**19	18	71	35
**23	22	73	8
**29	28	79	13
31	15	83	41
37	3	89	44
41	5	**97	96
43	21		

There is a story circulating about the famous British
mathematician G. H. Hardy and his meeting with the bright
young Indian mathematician Ramanujan.
Hardy told how he had ridden in a taxi with a number which
he considered very dull. Upon hearing the number Ramanujan
promptly replied how really interesting the number was after
all. He claimed it was the smallest integer which could be
written as the sum of two cubes in two different ways!

Write a program to find the number on Hardy's taxi.

Trial and error solutions are certainly permissible, a bit
of historical research wouldn't hurt either.

Essentially what you are looking for is an integer I

such that $I = X^3 + Y^3$

and

$I = A^3 + B^3$

where X ≠ A at the same time that Y ≠ B
or   Y ≠ B at the same time that X ≠ A

assume that X, Y, A, B belong to the
natural numbers.

Prepare a program that will construct a multiplication table for any base from 2 to 10.

Have the computer accept a number from an INPUT statement and from that construct the table.

HINT: Use a double subscripted variable and keep in mind that element $A(m,n) = A(n,m)$.

REFERENCES:

A PANORAMA OF NUMBERS, Robert Wisner, P. 10-18, Scott, Foresman & Co., Glenview, Illinois; 1970

RECREATIONS IN THE THEORY OF NUMBERS, A. H. Beiler, P. 67-72, Dover Publ. Co., New York; 1964

MATHEMATICAL PUZZLES AND PASTIMES, Aaron Bakst, P. 43-55, D. Van Nostrand Co., Inc., Princeton, N.J.; 1965

$$4_5 \times 2_5 = 13_5$$

Some numbers possess no status whatsoever, but when related to other numbers they become famous.

Such a number is 220. It doesn't appear to be unusual at all. In fact if we add up all of its integral divisors excluding the number itself we get:

  1 + 2 + 4 + 5 + 10 + 11 + 20 + 22 + 44 + 55 + 110 = 284

Nothing startling there, not yet. Now let's try another unassuming number, 284. If we do the same for it we get:

        1 + 2 + 4 + 71 + 142 = 220

A bit more intriguing isn't it? There seems to be a partnership here between 220 and 284; such number pairs are called amicable numbers. There are around 400 such number pairs known today. In 1750, Euler discovered 59 such pairs.

Devise a program to search out at least five more amicable pairs. There are at least five less than 10,000,000.

If in your research you find other pairs, they are allowable only if the computer program produces them in the normal course of its run.

You'll need a method of factoring into all the integral divisors, much as we suggested for perfect numbers. These two problems make an ideal tandem program. Be sure to exclude the number itself from the list.

REFERENCES:

MATHEMATICAL DIVERSIONS by J. A. H. Hunter, p. 2.

A PANORAMA OF NUMBERS, Robert J. Wisner, P. 101-103, Scott, Foresman and Company, Glenview, Illinois; 1970

RECREATIONS IN THE THEORY OF NUMBERS, A. H. Beiler, P. 26-30, Dover Publ. Inc., New York; 1964

HISTORY & DISCOVERY OF AMICABLE NUMBERS, Elvin J. Lee,P. 77 Journal of Recreational Mathematics, April 1972

Once you have figured out how to generate prime numbers
it should be a simple matter to modify the program and
print out a set of TWIN PRIMES. TWIN PRIMES are two
numbers both of which are prime and which differ by two.

There is only one even prime number and that is 2.
All other primes are odd. If two consecutive prime
numbers are found they are called <u>twin primes</u>.

For example, 3 & 5 are twin primes, so are 17 & 19.

Have your program 'spit out' all such pairs less than
say 2000.

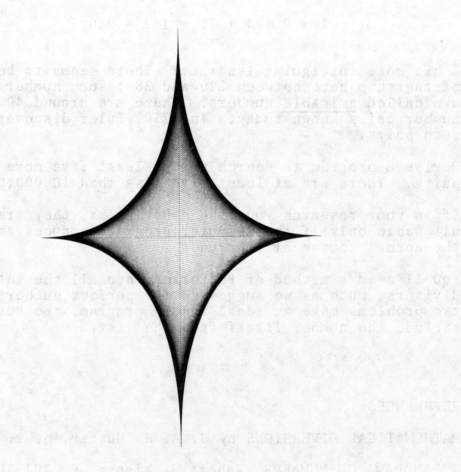

Write a program to invert an N x N matrix where N is no
bigger than five.

You may not use the MAT INV statement in the program for
anything but a check.

We have developed several algorithms for inverting a matrix,
any one of these are computer compatible. You might want
to check the inverse by using it to multiply the original
matrix and seeing if the identity matrix results. This is
quite easy to do with the series of MAT statements available
in BASIC.

REFERENCES:

BASIC PROGRAMMING, Kemeny & Kurtz, Chapter 16

PRINCIPLES OF COMPUTATION, Calingaert, P. 143-155

MORE CHIPS FROM THE MATHEMATICAL LOG, "Matrices", Kenneth
Loewen, P. 70, University of Oklahoma, Norman, Oklahoma; 1970

54 MAGIC SQUARES BY COMPUTER

A MAGIC SQUARE is an array of numbers with just as many rows as columns whereby the sum of any row, column or diagonal is always the same. No number may be used twice in constructing the array.

Write a computer program to generate magic squares up to 12 x 12. Let the user specify the size desired. The sum in question may be anything. It could possibly be selected by random numbers based on a starting point which the user specifies.

The MAGIC SQUARE shown below is remarkable in that it sums to a specific number for all rows, columns and diagonals but also for corner arrays and many more. It is the square attributed to Durer and appeared in one of his paintings.

16	3	2	13
5	10	11	8
9	6	7	12
4	15	14	1

Write a program to compute the day of the week a given date occurred on.

Input should include the month, day and year in any order you specify. You need not input the month alphamericaly.

Many useful algorithms have been developed to serve as perpetual calendars. Some research is required on your part here.

Set an upper and lower limit on the years; such as no later than 2500 A.D. and no earlier than 1600 A.D.

As an added attraction, use the program to show that the thirteenth day of any month is more likely to occur on Friday than on any other day.

An inability to develop your own algorithm may lead you to refer to the references below:

BASIC PROGRAMMING by Kemeny & Kurtz, Chapter 6, P. 36, Wiley & Sons, New York; 1971

MATHEMATICAL RECREATIONS AND ESSAYS, W. Ball, P. 449, MacMillan & Co.; 1914

MATHEMATICAL PUZZLES AND PASTIMES, Aaron Bakst, P. 84-96, D. Van Nostrand Co. Inc., Princeton, N.J; 1965

SCIENTIFIC AMERICAN, "Mathematical Games", Martin Gardner, Oct., 1967

The challenge to find an arithmetic progression containing exactly one-hundred terms, all of them distinct primes has so far eluded mathematicians.

So far the longest consists of only twelve terms with the initial term 23143 and a difference of 30030. It was dis-covered by W. A. Golubiev.

It would not be necessary here to break the record of twelve. Just find another sequence with at least seven terms, all of whose terms are distinct primes.

REFERENCES:

"SOME UNSOLVED PROBLEMS OF ARITHMETIC", 28th Yearbook of the NCTM, P. 211, W. Sierpinski, Washington, D.C.; 1963

A PANORAMA OF NUMBERS, Robert Wisner, P. 118-138, Scott, Foresman & Co., Glenview, Illinois; 1970

RECREATIONS IN THE THEORY OF NUMBERS, A. H. Beiler, P. 39-48, Dover Publishing Co., New York; 1964

Can you find numbers of the form $n2^n + 1$ called Cullen Numbers which for n>1 produce primes. Very recently it was shown that the least such prime was for n = 141.

Not only would you have to develop an algorithm to produce the exact digits of the number but you would also have to test its primeness.

REFERENCES:

"SOME UNSOLVED PROBLEMS OF ARITHMETIC", 28th yearbook of the NCTM, W. Sierpinski, Page 211, Washington, D.C.; 1963

A PANORAMA OF NUMBERS, Robert Wisner, P. 118-138, Scott, Foresman & Co., Glenview, Illinois; 1970

NCTM YEARBOOK #28 "Recent Information on Primes" Paul Rosenbloom, P. 34-45, Washington, D.C.; 1963

N factorial usually written N! or $\lfloor N$ may be defined as the product of the first N integers.

The beginning of a table for N! would look like this:

N	N FACTORIAL
1	1
2	2
3	6
4	24
5	120
6	720
7	5040
8	40320
9	362880
10	3628800

The problem is to carry this table out to 40!, while still retaining all digits of accuracy. N! increases quite rapidly with increasing N. A single variable in your program will not be able to contain all the digits.

You will have to devise a scheme to store the digits of N! in an array; one or two digits per element of the array. Then you will have to come up with a way of multiplying this array which represents a single large integer by N+1 to obtain the next (N+1) factorial.

Continue your table up to 40! or until one line of output is filled, whichever comes first.

The following approximation may prove helpful in setting the problem up.

STIRLING'S FORMULA

$$\sqrt{2n\pi}\,(n/e)^n < n! < \sqrt{2n\pi}\,(n/e)^n \left(1 + \left(\frac{1}{12n-1}\right)\right)$$

where $\pi = 3.14159...$, $e = 2.71828...$

Research this algorithm thoroughly before attempting the project.

Write a program to flip a coin any specified number of times.

Have the computer print out the actual result
of each flip; that is, H when a head occurs and T when
a tail occurs. Use a semi-colon (;) in your print
statement so as not to use 100 lines of paper in 100
flips. This will keep the printing element on the
same line.

Have the computer keep track of the number of
heads that occur and print out after the run how many
heads in how many tries. Finally compute the ratio
of heads to attempts. It should be very close to .5
for large N.

Suppose you agreed, as you were traveling along in a car, to write down the last two digits of the license plates of the next twenty cars to go by you.

One would have to agree that cars pass by completely at random in most situations. What do you think the chances are that in that group of twenty two-digit numbers, two of them will be the same? Remember there are 100 possible numbers from 00 to 99. You are going to record only the first twenty cars.

Write a computer program to compute the probability for any number of cars from 1 to 30, then have the computer generate license numbers at random. Use two letters, a blank and then four numbers. Generate random numbers and then use the CHR$ function to change those numbers into their coded alphameric equivalents. You can generate the numbers directly.

Look at your list and see how many matches there are. Then either modify or rewrite your program to generate the plates, print them out and then indicate how many and which ones match.

REFERENCES:

PROBABILITY AND STATISTICS, Fred Mosteller, Addison-Wesley, Reading, Massachusetts; 1961

INTRODUCTION TO PROBABILITY AND STATISTICS, Henry Alder P. 60-7, W. H. Freeman & Company, San Francisco; 1962

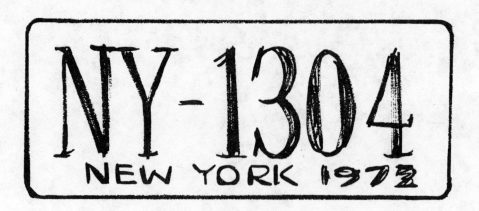

A telephone number has seven digits. The first two are usually limited in a given area to a certain sequence. Consider only the last five digits for this problem.

Compute the probability that in this 5 digit telephone number, two of the digits match. Remember, any one of 10 digits could fall in those five places. There are a total of 100,000 numbers which could occur, theoretically. Compute how many permutations of 10 digits will be needed to fill 5 spots. Divide this by 100,000 to get the probability.

Now write a computer program to generate 5 digit random numbers. Devise a routine to test their digits for a match. If you do not find one call it a Lola. Print out the number of Lolas in a group of random five digit numbers. Compute the percentage of Lolas and compare it to the predicted probability.

REFERENCES:

PROBABILITY AND STATISTICS, Fred Mosteller, Addison-Wesley, Reading, Mass.; 1961

INTRODUCTION TO PROBABILITY AND STATISTICS, Henry Alder, W. H. Freeman & Co., San Francisco; 1962

Zoerner L 17ConslRdClne -------869-6607
Zoll William L BeverwyckLatham --785-5232
Zoller Albert J Jr 10CaroIneLathm 785-7089
Zoller Albert J Sr JohnPTaylorApts 274-4325
Zoller Jos J SnydersLake ------283-1368
Zoltanski Joseph
          11DeerpathDrClne--869-3713
Zonitch J D 800-19thWvlt ------274-1420
Zonitch John 20BrentwdAv -----273-7242
Zonitch Mary Mrs 47CraigWvlt --273-5575
Zordan L J 6-9thWfd ----------237-5187
Zordan M J 12-9thWfd -------237-2541
Zorella A 2316-9thAvWvlt -------274-0455
Zorian Gregory T 397-4thAvNTy -235-5322
Zorian Mary A Miss
          1802-7thAvWvlt--271-8229

The area of a circle is πr^2. The area of a quadrant of that unit circle (circle with a radius of one) is one-fourth of πr^2.

Suppose we place that quadrant within a square as shown below. The area of the square is 1, while the area of the quadrant is as given above. If we were to generate points at random, so that every point fell within the confines of the square, it would either be within or outside the quarter-circle. In fact, it would depend on the ratio of their areas. If it were done a large number of times, the number of points falling within the quadrant as compared to the total number generated would tend to equal the ratio of the area of the quadrant to that of the square.

Derive an expression for that ratio which involves π. Then, program the computer to generate ordered pairs of random numbers. You will need a test for those points to determine whether they fall on or within the circle. (Count the circle as being within.) Vary the number of points you generate with an input statement. You will be intrigued to learn how many it actually takes to get a reasonable value for π.

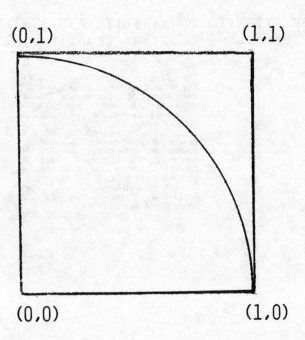

(0,1)   (1,1)

(0,0)   (1,0)

A series of parallel lines are ruled on a surface. The
distance between the lines is equal. A needle, whose
length is equal to the spacing of the lines is dropped onto
the surface. The probability that the needle crosses a
line, rather than lying entirely within a space is 2/π.

This has a number of interesting ramifications. It means
that we can estimate π with a series of random occurrences.
Dropping the needle a considerable number of times should
produce say X crossings. X is roughly = 2/π. So π is an
approximation to 2/X.

The horizontal position of the needle is immaterial. All
lines are identical. The following diagram may help you
set the problem up.
It represents the result of a single toss.

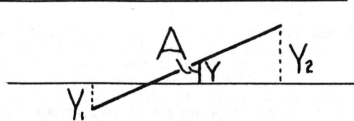

NOTE: *Needle
length exagger-
ated for clarity.*

Y is chosen as a random number between 0 and 1, since we
took the spacing of the lines as one unit. Then A is chosen
as a random number between -90° and +90°, that is between
-π/2 and +π/2 radians.

Y1 and Y2 are determined by trigonometry. If the integer
parts of Y1 and Y2 are different then the needle has crossed
the line. If the integer parts are the same then the needle
lies entirely within the spacing.

Write a program to do just that. Drop the needle a whole
bunch of different times and see how close to π you can come.

REFERENCES:

BASIC PROGRAMMING, Kemeny and Kurtz, P. 68, Wiley & Sons,
N.Y.; 1971

100 GREAT PROBLEMS OF ELEMENTARY MATHEMATICS, Heinrich Dorrie,
P. 73-75, Dover Press, New York; 1965

THE MATCHING BIRTHDAY PROBLEM

What is the probability that in a group of thirty people at least two have the same birthday? If you trust your intuition on this problem one would probably guess that it was low.

Most people are surprised to find that there is a p= .7 for a group of 30 people. In other words about 70% of the time there will be at least one matching set of birthdays in random groups of 30 people.

Derive an expression to compute the probability when the size of the group varies. Have the computer produce a table showing the probabilities for from 1 to 40 people. The formula will involve the product of the probabilities for each successive person.

Once you've generated the table and confirmed the 70% figure, you can verify it experimentally. You could interrogate a large number of groups of people and then record your successes and failures. You should be successful 70% of the time for a large number of trials.

With the computer however we can use random numbers. Generate random numbers between 1 and 365. Let these represent a given day of the year. In any group of 30 successive random numbers the probability of a match will be .7. Once you've generated 30 numbers test that group for a match. If successful increment the success parameter by 1. For a large number of simulations the number of successes divided by the total number of trials should just about equal the tabular probability for that number of people.

It's interesting to start out by letting the computer actually type the random numbers out, testing for a match being done by hand. You'll soon realize the value of having a routine in the program to do that for you.

REFERENCE: MATHEMATICS, TIME-LIFE BOOKS, Chapter on PROBABILITY.

In conjunction with the linear data regression one might want to know how closely two sets of scores are related. One might for example be interested in how the I. Q. scores and the College Board verbal achievements correlate.

A correlation coefficient, which is always less than 1 is used. The closer to one a number is the more close is the correlation. Correlation coefficients may also be negative, which would indicate sort of an inverse relation; such as the number of degrees on the thermometer and the number of gallons of fuel oil sold.

In order to compute the correlation coefficient one needs to know the following:

n = the number of scores
$\bar{x}$ = the arithmetic mean of the first set
$\bar{y}$ = the arithmetic mean of the second set
σx = the standard deviation of the first set of scores
σy = the standard deviation of the second set

Once these are known the coefficient can be computed using the following formula:

the correlation coefficient = r

$$-1 \leq r \leq 1 \quad \text{where} \quad r = \frac{\sum (x_i - \bar{x})(y_i - \bar{y})}{n \, \sigma_x \, \sigma_y}$$

REFERENCES: It is of the utmost importance that you read the following reference first. Alternate formulas along with the rationale behind the one given above are discussed along with the graphical significance.

PRINCIPLES OF COMPUTATION by P. Calingaert, pp. 78-80., Addison-Wesley Publ. Co.; 1965

A set of scores upon which you may wish to do the study appears in the appendix.

Write a program to find the arithmetic, geometric and harmonic means. Compare them.

Also, find the mean deviation from the mean.

There is a best way and order in which to compute the required quantities. For example, it is best to sum up the squares of the deviations in the same loop as the generation of those squares.

DO NOT generate a table of any intermediate data. Have the computer type out a list of the scores only, in order from lowest to highest.

REFERENCES:

The statistical sheet in the appendix of this volume.

Write a program to take the coefficients of a complex number in rectangular form: 'a + bi' and convert it to polar form.

The program should receive as input for this part only the variables 'a' and 'b'. Compute the modulus and the angle within your program.

The second part of the program should take any root of the complex number. Input here should only be what root is to be taken. Compute the roots with the numbers in polar form, then translate into rectangular form. Have the computer print all the roots (there will be N complex Nth roots) in rectangular form.

REFERENCE:

MODERN ANALYTICAL TRIGONOMETRY, Julian Mancill, P. 167-85, Dodd, Mead, and Company, New York; 1960

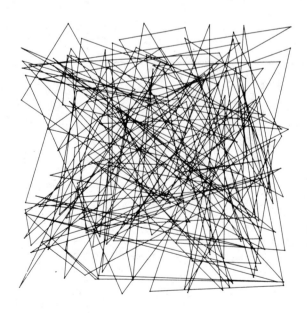

Suppose it is necessary to find the area under a curve between two vertical lines and the x-axis. The calculus tells us it can be done by integration. This is a difficult area to program on a digital computer. An equally accurate way would be to proceed as follows.

Imagine the x-axis to be the side of a rectangle, imagine that the lines x=a and x=b form the other pair of sides. It remains only to place a side parallel to the x-axis. That side should be placed so that it includes the curve in question (see below).

If one were to generate random numbers between the limits set down by the length and width of the rectangle then either of two situations would have to be true. If a pair of random numbers were to represent coordinates, that point would be within the rectangle and either above the curve or on or below it. The number of points falling on or below the curve would be in proportion to the area occupied by that sector within the rectangle. If one were to generate a sufficient numbers of points, the total below or on the curve divided by the total generated should be in the same proportion as the area beneath the curve is to the total area of the rectangle.

Write a program to calculate this area. You will need to input the limits a and b, the equation of the curve as well as the height of the rectangle. Make the height the maximum of a or b.

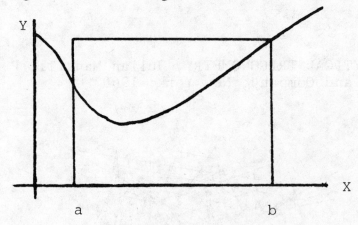

REFERENCE:

INTRODUCTION TO CALCULUS, Donald Greenspan, P. 196-206, Harper & Row, New York; 1968

Compute the area under a curve included between two vertical lines which represent the limits of integration. The area will be bounded by the curve, the vertical lines and the x-axis.

Break the area under the curve down into small trapezoids that are equal in height but have varying bases. Compute the area of each and sum them to approximate the area under the curve. Introduce the function into the program by means of a DEF FNA(X) statement.

As input you should include the limits of integration, the number of trapezoids, and the function to be integrated. Start with a small number of trapezoids and you will observe that the approximation, in most cases, becomes more accurate as the number of trapezoids increases.

There is no need to avoid functions whose upper limit is ∞. These can be taken care of by using a large number as an approximation to infinity.

If you've had any calculus, integrate the function and compare the value of the integral which represents the area under the curve to the computed value. It would be a real challenge to get the computer to integrate directly. This is a difficult problem.

REFERENCES:

        Almost any calculus text will have a discussion of the Trapezoidal Rule for function integration.

INTRODUCTION TO CALCULUS, Donald Greenspan, P. 196-206, Harper & Row, New York; 1968

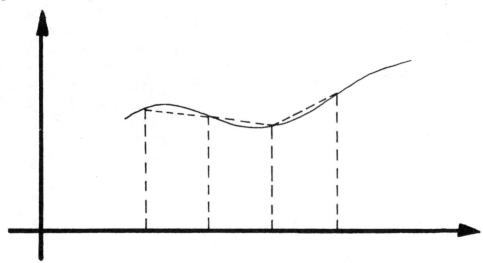

Write a computer program to print out the amount of energy available from a given unit of mass and its cost.

Use Einstein's famous formula: $E = mc^2$. Input the mass in kilograms. The constant 'c' will have to be in the proper units. Have the energy printed out in 'joules' and 'kilo-watt hours'. Assume that a 'kw-hour' costs 1¢.

The table should go from 10 to 100 kilos. The conversion factors should be available in any high school physics text.

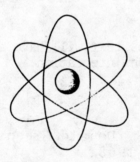

Write a program to print a table for converting from farenheit degrees to centigrade degrees and vice-versa.

Let the units on the left be integers. Use the entire type line for the table. The print-outs should be side by side to conserve paper. The formulas are famous and you should find them. Have the table go between whatever limits you think practical.

Label the columns so as to avoid confusion.

Einstein predicted that as a body's speed increased toward the velocity of light its mass would increase without limit according to the relationship given below.

He used this as a prediction of the fact that nothing could exceed the speed of light. He reasoned that at the speed of light the mass of the moving body would become infinite and would then require an infinite force to keep it in motion. Since no infinite forces exist, there could be no doubt that nothing with a mass can move at the velocity of light.

Some very tiny particles move very close to the speed of light. Write a program to compute for a given mass, just how much of an increase would take place as the velocity of the body increased up to 'c' - the velocity of light. Let your data be output in tabular form showing the velocity as a scalar and also as a function of its ratio to 'c'.

Look up the velocity of light in any system then keep 'v' in the same units. Mass units will be identical to the units you input for rest mass.

A similar formula exists for relative time dilation, and for linear contraction. These are known as Lorentz' Transformations. You may wish to investigate what happens to time as a body moves towards the speed of light.

v = velocity of the body
c = velocity of light
m_o = rest mass

m_r = relative mass

$$m_r = m_o \sqrt{\frac{1}{1 - \frac{v^2}{c^2}}}$$

REFERENCE: UNDERSTANDING PHYSICS, VOLUME I, FORCE, MOTION AND HEAT by ISAAC ASIMOV.

The following physics problem may seem to defy solution.

The diagram below is that of an infinite network of equal resisters. The difference of potential across the circuit is irrelevant. The idea is to find the total resistance of the network.

Remember resistances in series simply add up as they are, and resistances in parallel add up as reciprocals. Be sure to get the actual formulas exact.

THE CIRCUIT

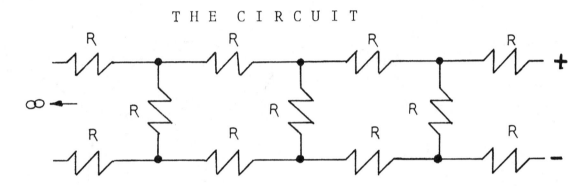

HINT: Careful study will lead you to the conclusion that a continued fraction will aid in the solution. Review what you know about them and let the computer evaluate the one you come up with. The answer involves the square root of three. Leave your answer in those terms.

REFERENCES:

BASIC PROGRAMMING, Kemeny and Kurtz, P 124-126, Wiley & Sons; New York; 1971

UNIVERSITY PHYSICS, Sears and Zemansky; Addison-Wesley Publ. Co.; Reading, Mass.; 1963

CONTINUED FRACTIONS by A. Ya. Khinchin; University of Chicago Press; Chicago; 1964

Write a program that will ask a young lover a few questions, and then write a letter to his girl friend on the basis of his answers.

INPUT statements of the form: 20 INPUT A$ are called for here. The remainder of the text is a problem for your own imagination.

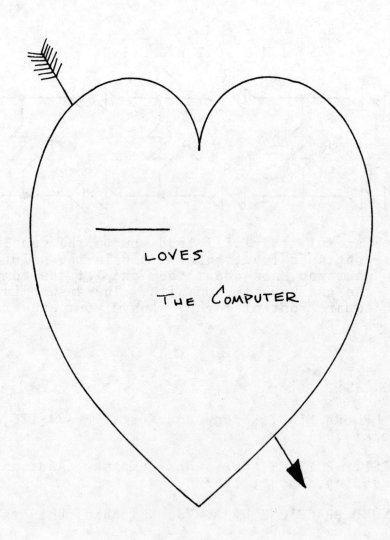

Write a program to sort a list of numbers entered at random.

The numbers may be any real numbers including zero and the negative reals. This is a required subroutine for most any statistical analysis. Remember numbers may appear more than once so take that into account.

This is an excellent exercise in using subscripted variables. It is a challenging program. Be sure to work the flow chart for this one out carefully. It will save considerable time and effort in the programming phase of the problem.

Do not use an INPUT statement here, it is quite time-consuming when used with extended data manipulation.

Include all data in a DATA statement at the end of the program.

A simple addition or modification to this program allows for the sorting of alphameric data (letters) which is a means of putting names etc. in alphabetical order.

REFERENCES:

The SMSG manual on ALGORITHMS & COMPUTATION discusses a few sorting routines.

So does - Mario Farina - Elementary BASIC with applications.

With the advent of the touch-tone phone came a new era in musical production. The tone put out by each button is equivalent to a note from the musical scale. Some phones have twelve buttons, some only ten. A respectable version of many songs can be generated using the proper sequence and timing of tones.

For example a fair version of "Raindrops Keep Fallin' on My Head" can be played by punching out 33363213. "Twinkle, Twinkle, Little Star" will result from tapping out 1199009. Even Beethoven's "Fifth Symphony" can be heard by 0005 8883.

Write a computer program to translate a song from ordinary sheet music into a respectable version suitable for the touch-tone phone. When experimenting be sure to call a friend before you start tapping, or you're liable to wind up with a bill for a long-distance call to East Kinorki.

The notes and their button equivalents are reproduced below.

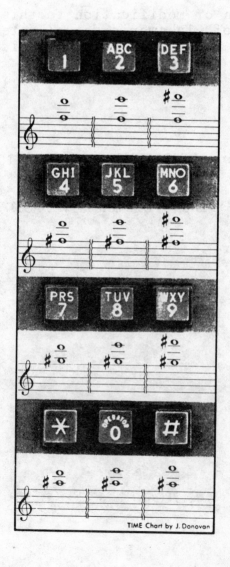

TIME Chart by J. Donovan

There is a trend in music to let the computer compose melodies and even lyrics for certain songs. These programs are rather involved musically speaking and are consistent in any number of aspects.

An interesting experiment would be to allow the computer to generate notes at random on a staff. The only check by the programmer would have to be regarding key and timing.

Have the computer type out a five line staff along with notes imposed upon it. If you wish you can draw the staff beforehand, or even insert a musical sheet side ways. Try to use different symbols for notes of different duration. A clever student might even be able to form the notes as they actually look. [o' or 0 or d' or some other concoction could be made to look like notes].

Attempts to play the music could lead to interesting interpretations in the right musical mind.

WRITE YOUR OWN CHECKS

    Write a program to produce a facsimile of a check. The face
value should be less than $100.

    Have the computer accept as INPUT the date, the payee, the
signator, the transit numbers and of course the amount of the check.
Remember this value must also appear in alphameric form in the
space beneath the payee. This may be accomplished by actually
typing the amount in words or by translating into alphamerics -
a most tedious operation.

    Dress your check up with a bank of your own creation.
Neatness counts!

    The check below is larger than actual size. Use the whole
width of the paper.

REFERENCES: Ask your father to borrow his check book.


```
*******************************************************************
*                                                                 *
*   EAST KINORKI ROD & GUN CLUB               NO.   69            *
*                                                                 *
*                             APRIL  1  1972    29-1             *
*                                               ————             *
*                                               1089             *
*                                                                 *
*   PAY TO  EUSTACIUS RIGGLETTS                    $  97.34       *
*                                                                 *
*                                                                 *
*   NINETY-SEVEN AND 34/100 ********************* DOLLARS         *
*                                                                 *
*   FIFTH NATIONAL BANK                                           *
*      YAMAHOO FALLS                                              *
*                                            ———X———             *
*   0213-001-13-435-17..                                          *
*******************************************************************
```

Program the computer to play Tic-Tac-Toe.

Allow the player the option of going first or second. Set
up a numbered array of the game board and work from there,
moves can be referred to by number and the player can do
his own bookwork. It takes too much computer time to con-
stantly print out the updated array.

Study the strategy of the game carefully. With proper
planning the worst the computer can do is draw. The
computers winning record affects the outcome of this problem
pointwise.

Allow for input by number and be sure the computer makes
it clear exactly how the moves should be entered. Inexper-
ienced people may be running this program.

```
   1  |  2  |  3
 ─────┼─────┼─────
   8  |  9  |  4
 ─────┼─────┼─────
   7  |  6  |  5
      |     |
```

The computer should be able to declare itself the winner
or admit that it's been drawn.

REFERENCE:

SCIENTIFIC AMERICAN, "Mathematical Games", Martin Gardner,
Vol. 225, No. 2; August 1971

A PALINDROME is a word or number which reads the same backwards or forwards.

The word 'otto' is a palindrome. So is the phrase, "Able was I 'ere I saw Elba."

Program the computer to test a phrase to see if it is a palindrome. Input the entire line as a string using a LINPUT statement. You can test numbers better than letters so convert the letters to their coded equivalents and test those from end-to-end.

The program should be capable of ignoring punctuation and spacing.

The United States is the only major industrial nation in the world which does not use the metric system of measurement. The day is not far off when we will convert to such a system. Every quantity will be represented as a decimal part of another. This will considerably simplify computation.

Getting used to such a system will be difficult. In anticipation of that day, write a program to convert a recipe in your cookbook [we certainly can't expect everyone to buy new cookbooks] from the units we use today into the less familiar metric units.

You might also consider writing in the opposite direction; for it is conceivable that outstanding recipes in future cookbooks would have to be bypassed unless you had a way to convert them into units for which you had the tools to cook and bake in.

A table of the major units in each system is given below.

```
1 Liter    =   1.0567 Quart

1 Kilogram = 2.205 Pounds
```

The ancient chinese game of NIM is a fascinating one.
Philosophers of the highest order used to play the game
for serious stakes.

Essentially the game goes like this. A pile of stones
is placed before each man. The pile may contain any number
of stones. The number is known to both players. (Fifteen
is a good number to get started with.)
Each man, at his turn, must take at least one and not more
than three stones. Players alternate until the last stone
is taken. The player who takes the last stone loses.

Program the computer to play NIM for a pile of fifteen
stones, marbles, lacrosse balls or whatever. Extra credit
will be given for a program which can play with any number
of objects. Make the program interactive, so that someone
with little knowledge of the computer or the game can under-
stand it.

REFERENCES: The instructional manual for the toy DR. NIM
should prove quite helpful.

PART ON NIM IN: BASIC PROGRAMMING, Kemeny & Kurtz, P. 78-81,
Wiley & Son, New York; 1971

A safe and educational method for gambling can be devised using the computer. Have the computer generate random numbers. Then devise a technique for translating these numbers into suit and rank. Be sure you keep track of what has been dealt. Perhaps you can teach the computer how to deal for a couple of forms of poker.

Leave as an option the number of cards to be dealt as well as drawn. A sophisticated version of this could also declare a winner and keep track of the bets and winnings.

Refer to the chart in the APPENDIX for the relative odds against and values of each type hand. It should be a program that will accomodate up to six people. Be sure the random number generator is set to produce a different set of random numbers each time. Otherwise the deck will never get shuffled.

REFERENCES: HOYLE'S GAMES, or any manual on card games.

Write a program that will receive two numbers separated by comma as input. These numbers will represent the time.

For example 10,43 could represent 10:43 o'clock.

Have the computer print the twelve numbers of the clock face in the proper order around a circle and have the hands properly positioned so as to indicate the time entered.

Be sure one hand is longer than the other, experiment with different symbols for maximum visibility and effect.

NOTE: No references necessary here. Just your own ingenuity.
        Don't worry about A.M. and P.M. The clock can't tell
        the difference, so why should you!

Write a program to transpose a melody from one key to any other key.

You'll have to devise a method of entering the original key along with a notation for sharps, flats and octaves.

Notes could be entered as letters which are subscripted. C1 could be middle C and C2 the next octave higher etc.

A more difficult rendition of the problem would involve printing out the transposed music on a staff. That would mean you would have to input the duration of notes and devise a scheme for printing them.

Take the digits 1 through 9, written in increasing order,
and insert between them either of the following three symbols:

    + (addition),   - (subtraction)   blank (run the digits)

Find all the different ways that will produce the arithmetic
value of 100.

One example is the one below:

$$1 + 23 - 4 + 56 + 7 + 8 + 9 = 100$$

Since there are three possibilities and eight spots to be
filled, there are 3^8 ways to test, that is 6561 possibilities.

About 10 of them will produce 100.

READABLE PAPER TAPE OUTPUT

The neophyte in computer circles is often confused and bewildered by the ASCII code (American Standard Code for Information Interchange). The actual configuration of holes in paper tape is practically undecipherable without a handbook.

Write a program to punch out on paper tape any alphameric (worded) expression which you may input. Some BASIC compilers have CHANGE statements which could prove helpful. Some time-sharing companies also have subroutines available to do such things.

It is a difficult and time-consuming task and is not mathematical in its nature. It is however an outstanding exercise in statement manipulation and is not beyond the scope of the talented student.

Give the computer a simple but adequate vocabulary list.

Have the computer compose some short verses of poetry.
This can be done by a random selection process or by more
careful choosing. Be sure to develop a rhyme scheme or
scanning pattern and develop an algorithm to test the
grammatical nature of your sentences.

Try to limit your sequences to grammatically possible ones.
The Japanese verse form containing exactly 17 syllables,
known as 'haiku', may be worth investigating.

Your English teacher may wish to collaborate.

Try to find three integers 'x', 'y' and 'z' such that:

$$(x + y + z)^3 = xyz$$

None of the three may equal zero. The problem originally proposed by Werner Mnich, a student at Warsaw University, is to prove that three rationals 'u', 'v' and 'w' exist such that:

$$u + v + w = uvw = 1$$

Mnich transformed both of the above equations into an equivalent question; that is whether there existed three integers 'a', 'b' and 'c' such that:

$$\frac{a}{b} + \frac{b}{c} + \frac{c}{a} = 1$$

The proof of any of the above would be a solution to one of the unsolved problems of arithmetic.

HINT: Solution of the equation involving integers is to be recommended. Loops are ideally suited to integral problems because it is possible to include all integers between specified limits. Since the rationals and the reals are "everywhere dense" problems of this nature are out.

REFERENCES:

"SOME UNSOLVED PROBLEMS OF ARITHMETIC", W. Sierpinski, Chapter 17 of the 28th yearbook of the NCTM, Washington, D.C.; 1963

TWO MORE OF THE UNSOLVED PROBLEMS OF ARITHMETIC

A couple of problems that look like quickies but really aren't.

1) Do there exist any solutions to the equation $X^X - Y^Y = Z^Z$ where X, Y, and Z are odd and greater than 1?

2) Do there exist three successive natural numbers each of which is a power of a natural number (exponent greater than 1)?

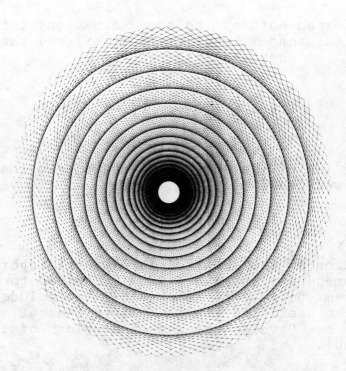

Appendix

A TRIGONOMETRIC GENERATION OF PASCAL'S TRIANGLE

n	sin(nx) + cos(nx)	coefficients
1	$[1] \cos x + [1] \sin x$	1 1
2	$[1] \cos^2 x + [2] \sin x \cos x - [1] \sin^2 x$	1 2 1
3	$[1] \cos^3 x + [3] \sin x \cos^2 x - [3] \sin^2 x \cos x$ $- [1] \sin^3 x$	1 3 3 1
4	$[1] \cos^4 x + [4] \sin x \cos^3 x - [6] \sin^2 x \cos^2 x$ $- [4] \sin^3 x \cos x + [1] \sin^4 x$	1 4 6 4 1
⋮	⋮	⋮

a) This is not simply a remake of the binomial theorem. As it turns out

   $\sin(nx) + \cos(nx) \neq (\sin x + \cos x)^n$ for all 'n'.

b) Investigate the following however: the sine and cosine can be related as follows,

   $[\cos(nx) + i \sin(nx)] = (\cos x + i \sin x)^n$ where $i^2 = -1$.

   The above is known as DEMOIVRE'S THEOREM!

ASCII CHARACTER CODE
(Decimal Value)

Decimal Value	ASCII Character		Decimal Value	ASCII Character	
32	SP	SPACE	64	@	
33	!		65	A	
34	"		66	B	
35	#		67	C	
36	$		68	D	
37	%		69	E	
38	&		7Ø	F	
39	'	APOSTROPHE	71	G	
4Ø	(		72	H	
41	)		73	I	
42	*		74	J	
43	+		75	K	
44	,	COMMA	76	L	
45	−		77	M	
46	.		78	N	
47	/		79	O	
48	Ø		8Ø	P	
49	1		81	Q	
5Ø	2		82	R	
51	3		83	S	
52	4		84	T	
53	5		85	U	
54	6		86	V	
55	7		87	W	
56	8		88	X	
57	9		89	Y	
58	:		9Ø	Z	
59	;		91	[	
6Ø	<		92	\	Backslash
61	=		93	]	
62	>		94	^	or ↑
63	?		95	_	or ←

93

SUMMARY OF STATISTICAL MEASURES

MEASURES OF CENTRAL TENDENCY:

ARITHMETIC MEAN $= \dfrac{\Sigma x_i}{N} = \overline{x}$

MEDIAN = the middle score for odd N
the mean of the two middle
scores for even N

MODE = the most frequent score

MEAN - MODE $\triangleq$ 3(MEAN - MEDIAN)

GEOMETRIC MEAN $= \sqrt[N]{x_1 * x_2 * x_3 * \ldots * x_N} = G$

HARMONIC MEAN $= \dfrac{1}{\dfrac{1}{N} \Sigma \dfrac{1}{x_i}} = H$

ROOT MEAN SQUARE $= \sqrt{\dfrac{\Sigma x_i^2}{N}} = RMS$

$H < G < X$

MEASURES OF DISPERSION:

RANGE $= x_N - x_1$ when scores are ordered & $x_1 < x_N$

MEAN DEVIATION FROM MEAN $= \dfrac{\Sigma |x_i - \overline{x}|}{N}$

VARIANCE $= \dfrac{\Sigma |x_i - \overline{x}|^2}{N} = \sigma^2$

STANDARD DEVIATION $= \sqrt{variance} = \sigma$

COEFFICIENT OF VARIATION $= \dfrac{\sigma}{x}$

M.D.M. $\triangleq \dfrac{4\sigma}{5}$

FOR A NORMAL DISTRIBUTION: $68.27\% \equiv \overline{x} \pm \sigma$

$95.45\% \equiv \overline{x} \pm 2\sigma$

$99.73\% \equiv \overline{x} \pm 3\sigma$

I. Q.

132	532
126	538
127	591
117	446
127	538
120	433
125	696
125	591
133	506
119	499
122	519
134	650
123	525
125	387
122	519
120	446
132	519
134	492
126	637
141	598
141	545
114	420
110	486
141	486
128	611
118	453
123	453
128	644
121	571
121	578
122	433
125	578
126	552
132	630
132	552
134	708
127	506
121	512
138	650
125	499
132	519
108	511
121	446
128	677
123	617
126	644
125	584
122	479
120	519
133	571

N = 50

NOTE: It is important that the scores remain paired. It is necessary to order the scores for a regression analysis, but you can only order one set for a correlation study.

Close inspection of the formula for correlation will lead you to conclude that order is unimportant unless the analysis is done by 'ranking'.

SAT
VERBAL

ODDS AGAINST DRAWING A CERTAIN POKER HAND

HAND	NUMBER POSSIBLE	ODDS
ROYAL FLUSH	4	649,739 to 1
STRAIGHT FLUSH	36	72,192 to 1
FOUR OF A KIND	624	4,164 to 1
FULL HOUSE	3,744	693 to 1
FLUSH	5,108	508 to 1
STRAIGHT	10,200	254 to 1
THREE OF A KIND	54,912	46 to 1
TWO PAIR	123,552	20 to 1
ONE PAIR	1,098,240	4 to 3
NOTHING	1,302,540	EVEN
ALL POSSIBLE HANDS	2,598,960	

ASCII CODE FOR EIGHT CHANNEL PAPER TAPE
(EVEN PARITY)

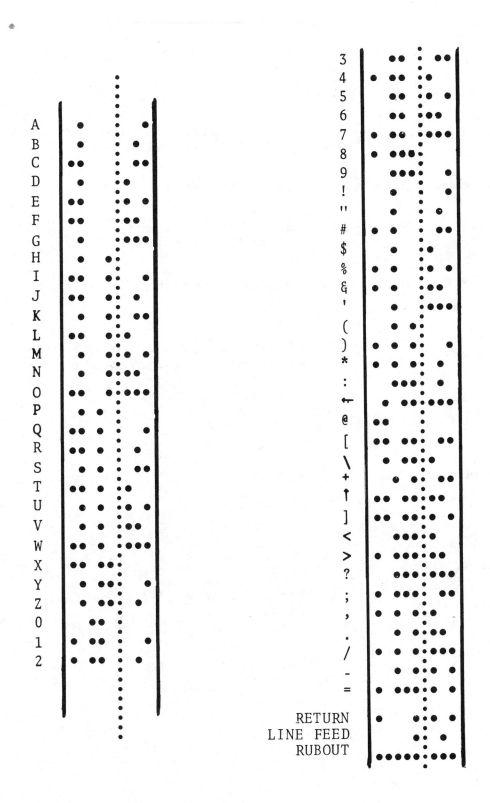

1. To sum a group of numbers:

    10 S=S+A   *where "A" is the current value of the*
                      variable and "S" is the partial sum.

2. Test for divisibility:

    20 IF X/K=INT(X/K) THEN ....   *is true when "X" is*
                                   divisible by "K".

3. To compute the values after division:

    30 R=X-INT(X/A)*A   *makes "R" the remainder when X is*
                         divided by A.

4. To exchange the values of two variables:

    40 S=10   *Lines 60,70 and 80 execute the*
    50 T=12   *exchange by assigning the value*
    60 W=S   *of S to W, T as the new S, and*
    70 S=T   *W (old S) as T.*
    80 T=W

5. To compute small factorials:

    90 I=1
    100 FOR X=1 TO N   *Factorial N will be the final*
    110 I=I*X   *value of I.*
    120 NEXT X
    130 END

6. To execute from a program with a string test:

```
140 INPUT A$
150 IF A$="YES" THEN STOP
```
Execution will stop when "YES" is input.

7. To decompose an integer into its digits:

```
160 X=123
170 A=INT(X/100)
180 B=INT(.1*(X-100*A)
190 C=X-100*A-10*B
```
A is hundreds digits of X,
B is tens digits of X,
C is units digit of X.

8. To compute compound interest directly:

```
200 FOR X=1 TO N
210 I=P*R
220 P=P+I
230 NEXT X
```
Where "R" is rate of interest,
"I" is amount of interest and
"P" is the principal.

9. To generate random numbers within a certain range:

```
240 RANDOMIZE
250 T=INT(((B-A)+1)*RND)+A
```
"B" must be greater than "A".

10. To round numbers:

```
260 X=INT(X+.5)
```
"X" to nearest integer.

```
270 X=(INT(10*X+.5))/10
```
"X" to nearest tenth.

11. To convert angle measure:

```
290 R=D/57.295779
```
"D" degrees to "R" radians.

```
300 D=57.295779*R
```
"R" radians to "D" degrees.

12. To compare two numbers when truncation errors are likely:

    310 IF ABS(B-X)<.00001 THEN ...   *will act as though*
                                             "B" equals "X".

13. To conserve paper when printing:

    320 PRINT B(X);   *will print multiple*
                                             values of B(X) on a line.

14. To find the area of a triangle when only its
    sides are known:

    330 S=(A+B+C)/2   *where "A", "B", and "C"*
    340 T=SQR(S*(S-A)*(S-B)*(S-C))   *are sides, "T" is area.*

15. To find the antilogs of a base 10 logarithm:

    350 Y=10↑X   *"Y" is antilog of "X".*

16. To convert the base of logarithms

    360 DEF FNL(X)=LOG(X)/LOG(10)   *gives base 10 logarithms*
                                             when LOG is base e.

    370 DEF FNL(Y)=LOG(Y)/LOG(A)   *gives base "A" logarithms*
                                             when LOG is logarithm to
                                             any other base Y.

17. When multiplying fractions do not multiply numerators
    and denominators and then divide: divide first and then
    multiply the decimals.

18. Do not try to decompose a number into its individual
    digits when it is possible to recompose the digits
    back to the number.

Bibliography

*Albrecht, R.L., Finkel, L. and Brown, J.R. <u>Basic For Home
      Computers</u>. New York: John Wiley & Sons, 1978. ($5.95)

*Ahl, David H. <u>Basic Computer Games</u>. Morristown, N.J.: Creative
      Computing Press, 1978. ($7.50)

*_____. <u>The Best of Creative Computing, Volume 1</u>. Morristown,
      N.J.: Creative Computing Press, 1976. ($8.95)

*_____. <u>The Best of Creative Computing, Volume 2</u>. Morristown,
      N.J.: Creative Computing Press, 1977. ($8.95)

*_____. <u>More Basic Computer Games</u>. Morristown, N.J.: Creative
      Computing Press, 1979. ($7.50)

Alder, Henry. <u>Introduction to Probability and Statistics</u>. San
      Francisco: W.H. Freeman and Co., 1962.

Amir-Moez, A.R. "Rational Approximations of Pi." <u>More Chips
      from the Mathematical Log</u>. Norman, Okla.: University of
      Oklahoma Press, 1970.

Asimov, Isaac. <u>Understanding Physics: Motion, Sound and Heat</u>
      New York: New American Library, 1969.

Bakst, Aaron. <u>Mathematical Puzzles and Pastimes</u>. Princeton:
      D. Van Nostrand Co., Inc., 1965.

Ball, W. <u>Mathematical Recreations and Essays</u>. London: MacMillan
      and Co., 1914.

Bashaw, W.L. <u>Mathematics for Statistics</u>. New York: John Wiley
      and Sons, 1969.

Beiler, A.H. <u>Recreations in the Theory of Numbers</u>. New York:
      Dover Publishing Co., 1970.

Caldwell, J. H. <u>Topics in Recreational Mathematics</u>. Cambridge:
      Cambridge University Press, 1966.

Calingaert, Peter. <u>Principles of Computation</u>. Reading, Mass.:
      Addison-Wesley Publishing Co., 1965.

Davis, Phillip. <u>Lore of Large Numbers</u>. New York: Random House,
      1961.

Dorrie, Heinrich. 100 Great Problems of Elementary Mathematics. New York: Dover Publishing Co., 1965.

*Dwyer, Thomas and Critchfield, Margot. Basic and the Personal Computer. Reading, Mass.: Addison-Wesley Publishing Co., 1978. ($12.95)

* _____ . and Kaufman, Michael S. A Guided Tour of Computer Programming in Basic. Boston: Houghton Mifflin Company, 1973. ($12.95)

Ehle, B.R. Elementary Computer Applications. New York: John Wiley & Sons, 1971

Gardner, Martin. "Mathematical Games." Scientific American. Vol. 225, No. 2, August 1971.

Greenspan, Donald. Introduction to Calculus. New York: Harper and Row, 1968.

*Gruenberger, Fred and Jaffray, George. Problems for Computer Solution. New York: John Wiley & Sons, 1965. ($12.50)

Keedy, M. Algebra and Trigonometry. New York: Holt, Rinehart and Winston, 1967.

*Kemeny, John G. and Kurtz, Thomas E. Basic Programming, Second Edition. New York: John Wiley & Sons, 1971. ($10.50)

Khinchin, A. Ya. Continued Fractions. Chicago: University of Chicago Press, 1964.

Kraitchik. Mathematical Recreations. New York: W.W. Norton and Co., 1942.

Lee, Elvin J. "History and Discovery of Amicable Numbers." Journal of Recreational Mathematics. April, 1972.

Lee, John. Numerical Analysis for Computers. New York: Reinhold Publishing Co., 1966.

LeVeque, William. Elementary Theory of Numbers. Reading, Mass.: Addison-Wesley, 1962.

Loewen, Kenneth. "Matrices." More Chips from the Mathematical Log. Norman, Okla.: University of Oklahoma Press, 1970.

Mancill, Julian. Modern Analytical Trigonometry. New York: Dodd, Mead and Company, 1960.

Meyer, J.S. Fun with Mathematics. Cleveland: World Publishing Co., 1952.

_____. _More Fun with Mathematics_. Cleveland: World Publishing Co., 1952.

Moise, Edwin. _Geometry_. Reading, Mass.: Addison-Wesley Publishing Co., 1967.

Mostellier, Fred. _Probability and Statistics_. Reading, Mass.: Addison-Wesley Publishing Co., 1961.

Newman, James. _The World of Mathematics_, 4 volumes. New York: Simon and Schuster, 1956.

Niven, Ivan. _Introduction to Computing Through the Basic Language_. New York: Holt, Rinehart and Winston, 1969.

Ore, O. _Invitation to Number Theory_. New York: Random House, 1967.

Ruckstahl, Kathy and Wilford, Charles. "Prime Numbers: Yes, No, Perhaps." _More Chips from the Mathematical Log_. Norman, Okla.: University of Oklahoma Press, 1970.

*Sage, Edwin R. _Fun and Games with the Computer_. Newburyport, Mass: Entelek, Inc., 1975. ($8.95)

*_____. _Problem-Solving with the Computer_. Newburyport, Mass.: Entelek, Inc., 1969. ($8.95)

Sears and Zemansky. _University Physics_. Reading, Mass.: Addison-Wesley Publishing Co., 1963.

Selby, Samuel. _CRC Standard Mathematical Tables_. Cleveland: Chemical Rubber Co., 1965.

Sierpinski, W. "Some Unsolved Problems of Arithmetic." _28th Yearbook of the NTCM_. Washington, D.C., 1963.

*Spencer, Donald D. _Fun with Computers and Basic_. Ormond Beach, Fla.: Camelot Publishing Co., 1977. ($7.95)

*_____. _Using Basic in the Classroom_. Ormond Beach, Fla.: Camelot Publishing Co., 1978. ($11.95)

Stein, Edwin. _Fundamentals of Mathematics_. Boston: Allyn and Bacon, 1967.

Stewart, B.M. _Theory of Numbers_. New York: MacMillan and Co., 1964.

*Taylor, Jason. _The Calculus with Analytic Geometry Handbook_. Bedford, Mass.: Taylor Associates, 1976. ($2.95)

*Townsend, Charles Barry. Merlin's Puzzlers. Maplewood, N.J.:
     Hammond, Inc., 1976. (Two volume set $7.50)

*Wickelgren, Wayne A. How to Solve Problems. San Francisco:
     W.J. Freeman and Company, 1974. ($7.50)

 Wilson, W.A. Analytic Geometry. Boston: D.C. Heath and Co.,
     1949.

 Wisner, Robert. A Panorama of Numbers. Glenview, Ill.: Scott
     Foresman and Co., 1970.